GILBERT SHELTON
the FABULOUS FURRY

FREAK

BROTHERS
COLLECTION THREE

KNOCKABOUT

HAVE A GOOD ONE LUV'!! (FNAAR FNAAR

love Andy xxx

& Darryl xo

contents

MORE ADVENTURES OF THE
FABULOUS FURRY FREAK BROTHERS

Violence on the Bus
Grass Roots
Organic Mechanic
The Mellow Cab Man
The 4th Freak Brother
and lots more

Design by Rian Hughes. **Send
for free illustrated catalogue.** ISBN 086166 067 6. Printed in
Denmark.

3

to be continued...

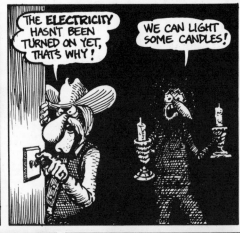

5

to be continued...

7

9

What **have** the Fabulous Freaks purchased? A 27-acre "spread" in the Shark River National Unreachable Wilderness Area, right on the very banks of the afore-mentioned watercourse itself...

WELL, I'M GOING FOR A LITTLE FLOAT DOWNSTREAM ON MY **INFLATABLE BOAT!**

I WONDER WHY THEY CALL IT THE SHARK RIVER?

WHOOPS! DROPPED TH' DARN THING!

BOUNCE

BOUNCE

I THOUGHT THE REALTOR SAID **FORTY** ACRES!

WELL, IT WOULD BE ABOUT FORTY IF IT WERE LAID OUT FLAT!

RIP GOBBLE CHEW

!

BURP

GOSH, I'M GETTING COLD!

THE SUN WENT BEHIND THE MOUNTAINS!

GEE, THAT'S THE FIRST SUNSET I'VE EVER SEEN AT **2:30** IN THE AFTERNOON!

I'M HUNGRY!

WE ATE UP ALL THE SALAMI AND RITZ CRACKERS ALREADY?!!

WELL, I'LL TAKE THE TRUCK TO THE "SEVEN-ELEVEN" AND PICK UP SOME TEEVEE DINNERS AND SOME BEER...

ARE YOU KIDDING? HAVE YOU FORGOTTEN THAT THERE ARE **75 MILES** OF MOUNTAIN DIRT ROADS BETWEEN HERE AND THE NEAREST FOOD STORE?

...AND WE COULDN'T HEAT A TEEVEE DINNER ANYWAY SINCE THERE'S NO **OVEN!**

THERE AREN'T ANY LIGHTS, EITHER, SINCE THERE'S NO **ELECTRICITY!**

AND WITH THE ADVENT OF **DARKNESS** COME THE SMOTHERING CLOUDS OF ARCTIC MOSQUITOS!

ZZZ

YOW! YOW!

I'VE NEVER SEEN SUCH LARGE MOSQUITOS!

THEY'RE SWARMING THROUGH THE WINDOW HOLES!

RUN! RUN! WE'LL TAKE REFUGE IN THE CAMPER!

I HADN'T REALIZED JUST HOW **SMALL** THIS CAMPER REALLY WAS!

GET YOUR **FOOT** OUT OF MY FACE!

OOPS! EXCUSE ME!

Z.

PLEASE! THAT'S PART OF ME!

SNORE! TWEET!

CONTINUED IN TWO WEEKS...

13

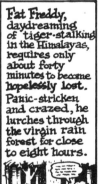

LATE THAT EVENING, AFTER THEIR CHORES ARE FINISHED, FRANKLIN AND PHINEAS HOLD A CAUCUS FOR THEIR MINORITY GROUP BY THE KITCHEN STOVE.

WE GOTTA **REWRITE** THIS HERE **CONSTITUTION!**

YEAH! THIS **HOUSEWORK** IS A REAL **PAIN!**

(AHEM!) **ATTENTION, COMMUNE!** WE SHALL NOW CALL FOR A VOTE ON THE ADOPTION OF THIS **NEW CONSTITUTION,** AS SUBMITTED BY YOURS TRULY, FREEWHEELIN' FRANKLIN, ESQ., WHICH CALLS FOR THE **PERMANENT DIVISION** OF **LABOR** ACCORDING TO **NATURAL** LINES OF **DIVISION!**

NEW CONSTITUTION

BE IT RESOLVED, HENCEFORTH AND FOREVERMORE, THAT THE COMMUNAL CHORES BE PERFORMED IN ACCORDANCE WITH THE ANCIENT, HONORABLE, AND NATURAL LAW, MEANING THAT THE WOMEN SHALL DO THE COOKING, SWEEPING, AND WASHING, AND THAT THE **MEN** SHALL BE IN CHARGE OF **DEFENSE!**

THAT'S THE MOST **BLATANTLY SEXIST** IDEA I'VE **EVER HEARD** IN MY **LIFE!** IF YOU'RE TRYING TO BE **FUNNY,** WE ARE **NOT AMUSED!** YOU GUYS START SPOUTING THAT SEXIST LINE IN OUR COMMUNE, AND YOU JUST MIGHT FIND YOURSELVES SLEEPING **ALL ALONE** TONIGHT!

I'M **SERIOUS,** BELLA! I'M CALLING FOR AN **OFFICIAL COMMUNE VOTE, RIGHT NOW!**

I MEANT WHAT I SAID, YOU GUYS! VOTE **SEXIST** AND YOU **SLEEP ALONE!** WE **WOMEN** WILL **STICK TOGETHER,** I **PROMISE** YOU!

ALL RIGHT! OFFICIAL VOTE! ALL IN FAVOR RAISE YOUR HANDS!

C'MON, FREDDY! IT'S **VOTING TIME!**

17

18

19

BACK IN THE HOUSE, THE YOUNG WOMEN CRINGE IN TERROR AS A BLOOD-CURDLING CRY SPLITS THE NIGHT.

EEEEYARRGGHHH!

THAT'S FREDDY'S VOICE!

SCREEEEEEEEEEAM! BAWLLLLL! ARGGGGGHH!!

STOP IT, FELLOWS! I'M SORRY I VOTED AGAINST YOU! I CHANGE MY VOTE OFFICIALLY! YOW!

THEY'RE TORTURING HIM!

20

CHANGING YOUR VOTE ISN'T ENOUGH, FAT FREDDY! WE'RE NOT GOING TO STOP UNTIL THE WOMEN CHANGE THEIR VOTE, TOO!

NO! NO! PLEASE!

OH GHOD, I CAN'T STAND IT ANY LONGER!

SHRIEK!

CHOKE!

MY GOD, WHAT KIND OF SADISTIC THING ARE THEY DOING TO HIM?

LISTEN, FRANKLIN AND PHINEAS! WE GIVE UP! WE CAN'T STAND TO HEAR FREDDY'S PITIFUL SHRIEKS ANY LONGER! PLEASE STOP! WE'LL DO ANYTHING YOU SAY! JUST STOP WHATEVER IT IS YOU'RE DOING TO POOR FREDDY!!!

BLEAT WARBLE ULULATE

OKAY, PUT THE FOOD AWAY, PHINEAS!

THUS DID THE FREAK BROTHERS AVOID AN EMBARRASSING REPEAT OF LYSISTRATA'S ANCIENT VICTORY OVER THE FORCES OF WAR.

21

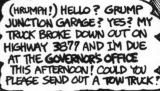

24

26

27

The rumor of GOLD in the creek has brought THOUSANDS of PEOPLE, not to mention MILLIONS of DOLLARS, into the Shark River National Unreachable Wilderness Area.

WHAT IS IT ABOUT PEOPLE THAT MAKES THEM HANG AROUND DAY AFTER DAY, WHEN NOBODY HAS FOUND ANY GOLD AT ALL?

IT'S CALLED "GOLD FEVER," FREIDA.

I'M BEGINNING TO GET A LITTLE PARANOID ABOUT ALL THIS MONEY WE'VE COLLECTED!

MAYBE WE OUGHT TO BURY IT!

NOT A BAD IDEA!

THE WILDERNESS IS BEGINNING TO CRAWL WITH PEOPLE!

RUSH CITY

GROCERIES · LOANS · PAWN

SALOON

THERE'S NO GOLD! I TELL YOU, NO GOLD!

NO GOLD!

NO GOLD!

NO GOLD...

IT'S NO USE, FAT FREDDY! NO ONE BELIEVES YOU! AND WHY SHOULD THEY EVEN CARE, ANYHOW? THEY HAVE A GREAT TOURIST THING GOING!

GOLD NUGGET HOTEL

X-RATED FILMS · WATERBEDS · ASTROTURF

OPEN

RIDES 1 BLOCK

2 SHOWS EVERY HOUR

BUS TOURS

WAX MUS[EUM]

WILD WEST SHOW

Coming Soon! KIDDIE LAND

Madame OLGA

SAY, BUDDY, IF YOU WAS WILLING TO SELL, I MIGHT GIVE YOU FIFTY THOUSAND DOLLARS FOR THAT PROPERTY!

LET'S SELL! LET'S SELL!

ER, UH... NOPE! WE'RE ASKING TWO HUNDRED THOU!

31

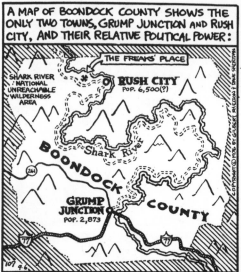

A MAP OF BOONDOCK COUNTY SHOWS THE ONLY TWO TOWNS, GRUMP JUNCTION AND RUSH CITY, AND THEIR RELATIVE POLITICAL POWER:

GRUMP JUNCTION, THE COUNTY SEAT, IS THOUGHT TO BE SOLIDLY BEHIND THE "DEMOCRATIC" INCUMBENT, SHERIFF GRUMP.

RUSH CITY, DEVELOPED ALMOST OVERNIGHT BY REAL ESTATE HUSTLERS, IS THOUGHT TO LEAN TOWARD "REPUBLICAN" BUFORD BUX.

BUT THE PREDICTIONS, AS WE ALL KNOW, DO NOT ALWAYS COME TRUE.

I'M GONNA WRITE IN THAT PHINEAS FREAKEARS FELLOW!

ME TOO! HOW DO YOU SPELL IT?

SO WHEN ELECTION DAY IS OVER AND IT IS TIME TO COUNT THE VOTES:

THIS MIGHT (GULP) TAKE A WHILE, FOLKS!

(CHOKE) MOST OF THE BALLOTS ARE WRITE-INS!

DID YOU HEAR? THE BALLOTS WERE MOSTLY WRITE-INS!

THAT COULD ONLY MEAN ONE THING!

EVERYONE OVER TO THE FREAK'S PLACE FOR THE VICTORY PARTY!

FOR HE'S A JOLLY GOOD FELLOW, FOR HE'S A JOLLY GOOD FELLOW

THE PEOPLE'S CHOICE SHERIFF PHINEAS FREAKEARS

P.F. IS OUR MAN

WE LIKE PHINE

FREAKER

PHINEAS, I'D LIKE YOU TO MEET THE GUY THAT RESCUED ME WHEN I WAS LOST IN THE WOODS THAT TIME...

HE MAKES A KIND OF PSYCHEDELIC MOONSHINE WHISKEY USING FERMENTED MUSHROOMS!

OH YEAH? COULD I HAVE A LITTLE TASTE OUT OF THAT BOTTLE?

SORRY, BUB, TOO LATE! BOTTLE'S EMPTY!

I ALREADY POURED IT IN THAT PUNCHBOWL OVER THERE!

FOR THE NEXT FOURTEEN HOURS THE VICTORY PARTY CONTINUES, FASTER AND FASTER, LOUDER AND LOUDER, WILDER AND WILDER, UNTIL IT IS ENOUGH TO SUMMON THE LONG-DEAD SPIRIT OF THE MERRY GREEK DIONYSIUS, WHO LEADS THE REVELERS IN MANY A RIBALD SONG AND DANCE...

FLASH FLOOD!!!

1116
10-4

EPILOGUE:
(BOONDOCK COUNTY)

ALTHOUGH RUSH CITY AND EVERYTHING ELSE FOR TEN MILES OF THE SHARK RIVER WAS COMPLETELY WASHED AWAY BY A **FLASH FLOOD**, A **NEW CITY** WAS PROMPTLY ERECTED ON THE **SAME** SPOT.

AND SURE ENOUGH, EVERY YEAR THERE IS ANOTHER FLASH FLOOD. THE NEW CITY IS COMPLETELY WASHED AWAY OVER AND AGAIN.

THE ANNUAL EVENT HAS BECOME A POPULAR SPECTACLE THAT BRINGS THOUSANDS OF TOURISTS EACH FALL ON THE NEWLY CONSTRUCTED FREEWAY.

AN EXPENSIVE HOME IN RUSH CITY IS CONSIDERED A STATUS SYMBOL EVEN AMONG THE ULTRA-WEALTHY, AND MANY ARE WRITTEN OFF AS TAX LOSSES YEARLY.

A LARGE RELIGIOUS CULT HAS GROWN UP AWAITING THE RE-APPEARANCE OF THEIR GOD, WHO THEY CLAIM APPEARED LIVE AT THIS SITE IN THE YEAR 1976.

39

THE FABULOUS FURRY FREAK BROTHERS

IN "THE PARAKEET THAT OUTWITTED THE D.E.A."

COPYRIGHT © 1977 BY GILBERT SHELTON
STORY: JOE BROWN

42

SPECIAL DELIVERY, REGISTERED AND INSURED, FOR SOMEONE NAMED "**DEAR SWEET FAT FREDDY!**" IS THIS A **JOKE**?

POSTMAN? PACKAGE? THAT'S **ME**! I'LL SIGN! GIVE IT HERE! I'LL SIGN! OH LORD! WHEW! THANK YOU!

WELL, SIGN IT, THEN, STRAWNOSE! HERE!

JEEZUS!

WELL, (AHEM)... SINCE WE'RE ALL OUT OF **DOPE** BECAUSE WE **WEREN'T BUSTED** (AND WHO AM I TO PLACE THE BLAME ON OUR IRRATIONAL ACTIONS), BUT WE **ARE BROKE**, AND I FEEL SO... SO... **SPRINGY**... I CAN'T EXPLAIN IT... I THINK I'LL GO OUT AND GET MYSELF A **JOB**!

WHO KNOWS WHY I FEEL THIS WAY! I NEVER WANTED A JOB **BEFORE**... COMET INSURANCE? EDSEL REPAIR? SAY, WHERE DID WE GET THAT NEAT **STATUE**? WELL, I'LL SEE YOU GUYS **LATER**, WHEN I'M **RICH**!

SLAM

GUESS I'LL SEE WHAT'S IN MY PACKAGE!

43

HE'LL PROBABLY FIND EIGHTEEN JOBS AND WE'LL HAVE TO HELP HIM!

BOY! THAT MDA, OR ACID, OR COKE, OR SOMETHING— COULD HAVE BEEN THE RUM, I SUPPOSE—SURE DOES COME ON FAST! THIS LOOKS LIKE A BIRD CAGE WITH A PARAKEET IN IT, AND A WHOLE BUNCH OF HUNDRED DOLLAR BILLS LINING THE BOTTOM OF THE CAGE!

WHAT? YOU'RE CRAZY! LOOK, THERE'S A LETTER ATTACHED! GIVE IT HERE! I'LL READ IT!

YOU'RE CRAZY! IT LOOKS LIKE A FEATHERED TOAD IN JAIL TO ME!

Dear Sweet Fat Freddy,
I realize you are unconventional and don't believe in birthday gifts, but you were born once (although I can't remember when) so here is your present! It's your Uncle Artie. I turned him into a parakeet. He will need 3½ gms. of parakeet food per day. If you lose 125 pounds, I'll send you $10,000.
love, Aunt Sally

GOOD LORD! THERE'S EIGHT HUNDRED DOLLARS IN THE BOTTOM OF THIS CAGE, ALL COVERED IN BIRDSHIT!

SHUT UP! YOUR AUNT PUT PRUNE JUICE IN MY WATER! I COULDN'T HELP IT!

NOW GO BUY ME SOME FOOD! YOU'LL NEED A GRAM SCALE TO WEIGH THE STUFF WITH!

HRUMPH! IDIOTS! SNORTED ALL OF THE COKE BECAUSE OF A POSTMAN! I SUPPOSE IF IT HAD BEEN A REAL BUST YOU WOULD HAVE EATEN THE FURNITURE! SUCH AS IT IS...

NOW, TURN THAT BONG BACK UPRIGHT, AND IF THERE'S ANY RESIDUE LEFT, BLOW THE SMOKE THIS WAY! AND GO GET THE FOOD AND THE GODDAM SCALE! HURRY!

WELL! HUH! I GUESS I'LL JUST **DO THAT**! I SEEM STRAIGHT ENOUGH, AND SINCE YOU **ARE** MY UNCLE **ARTIE**, A TALKING PARAKEET AND ALL, **RIGHT**? I'LL JUST GO WASH THE **BIRDSHIT** OFF THESE **HUNDREDS** AND BE ON MY **WAY**...

BABBLE BABBLE...

PUFF PUFF

AHHHHH!

THANKS A LOT, HAIRY, I NEEDED THAT!

WHEW, WHAT A TRIP! BIG STRONG MAN **ONE** MINUTE, DUMB FUCKING PARAKEET THE **NEXT**!

OL' SALLY'S A **VINDICTIVE** WOMAN!

SAY! WHY DO YOU WEAR THAT BIG **HAT** IN THE **HOUSE**? I MEAN, IF I WAS A **BUZZARD**, FULL OF PRUNE JUICE AND ALL, WHIZZING AND POOTING AROUND OVER YOUR **HEAD**, I COULD **UNDERSTAND**, BUT...

NEVER MIND THAT CRAP! NOW LET ME GET THIS STRAIGHT... FAT FREDDY'S **AUNT** TURNED YOU INTO A **PARAKEET**? YOU ARE **ACTUALLY TALKING** TO ME?

45

BET YOUR ASS, HAIRY! SHE'S A **WITCH**, THAT'S WHAT! I COULD TURN **YOU** INTO A DAMN FAG **SQUIRREL** IF SHE HADN'T TURNED ME INTO A PARAKEET! THE BITCH! SHE JUST CAUGHT ME WHILE I WAS **NAPPING**!

OH WELL, THAT'S LIFE...

THAT'S LIFE, AW HAW, THAT'S LIFE...

I SHOULD WRITE THIS DOWN... OR MAYBE I SHOULD JUST JUMP OUT THE WINDOW...

MEANWHILE, PHINEAS HAS BEEN TURNED AWAY EVERY PLACE HE HAS APPLIED FOR A JOB, AND NOW THE **COKE** IS **WEARING OFF.**

YOU! YOU'RE **PERFECT!** WE NEED ANOTHER **D.E.A. AGENT!** ONE HUNDRED DOLLARS A DAY **PLUS** EXPENSES! AND YOU GET YOUR OWN **D.E.A. IDENTIFICATION,** WHICH (HEH HEH) YOU CAN ALWAYS USE ANY WAY YOU LIKE! YOU'RE A **PERFECT** UNDERCOVER NARK!

WHAT? WAIT A MINUTE! I'M NO **COP!** GET AWAY FROM ME! WHERE'S YOUR **WARRANT?**

RELAX, PAL! I'M FROM **DEL RIO PRODUCTIONS, INC.!** WE'RE MAKING A **MOVIE!**

WE'RE A BUNCH OF **D.E.A. AGENTS,** YOU GET THE PICTURE, AND WE COME ACROSS THIS **PLANE** PARKED IN THE WOODS... WE **OPEN FIRE** ON THE SON OF A BITCH... CONFISCATE THE **DOPE... GREAT PROPAGANDA** FOR THE **AGENCY...** TOTALLY FEDERALLY FUNDED...

WE NEED ONE MORE SLOVENLY UNKEMPT UNDERCOVER NARC TO FILL OUT OUR CAST (WE'VE ALREADY CAST THE CLEAN-CUT SMUGGLERS) AND **YOU** FIT THE BILL **EXACTLY!**

HOW'S ABOUT IT, SPORT?

A HUNDRED DOLLARS A DAY? SURE! COUNT ME IN!

SAY, YOU WOULDN'T HAPPEN TO HAVE ANY OF THAT, UH, "CONFISCATED DOPE" ON YOU, WOULD YOU? UH, TO SORT OF HELP ME GET INTO THE "MOOD" OF THIS LITTLE VENTURE?

46

SURE, PAL... HERE'S SOME **COCAINE** WE'RE GOING TO "FIND" ON THE "SUSPECTS" LATER ON IN THE MOVIE! TAKE ALL YOU **NEED!**

AND HERE'S YOUR **I.D.**, YOUR **GUN**, YOUR **TEAR GAS**... **EVERYTHING YOU NEED!** IT'S ALL IN THE BAG! NOW LET'S GET TO WORK!

HOP IN!

HELLO, FELLAS!

MEANWHILE, **FAT FREDDY,** BAG OF PARAKEET SEED IN HAND, IS PASSING BY A **HEAD SHOP.**

MY, I HAVEN'T BEEN IN ONE OF **THESE** PLACES IN **YEARS!** THEY USED TO HAVE THOSE CRUDE LITTLE **POSTAL SCALES!** I COULD WEIGH UNCLE ARTIE'S **FOOD** THAT WAY!

COSMIC HAROLD'S **HEAD SHOP** No. 14

FAT FREDDY FAILS TO NOTICE THE CARLOAD OF **REAL** D.E.A. AGENTS SPYING ON THE SHOP'S CUSTOMERS, WAITING FOR A **BIG ONE.**

LOOKY! THAT **FAT** ONE'S SO HIGH HE CAN'T EVEN TOUCH THE GROUND WHEN HE WALKS!

COSMIC HAROLD'S
HEAD SHOP

IF THAT'S **PARAKEET SEED** IN THAT BAG, I'M AN **HONEST MAN!** LET'S BUST THE STORE!

COSMIC HA OLD'S
HEAD SHOP

NO! LET'S WAIT! THIS COULD BE SOMETHING REALLY BIG! OPEN UP SOME MORE BEERS AND LET'S SIT TIGHT!

I SAY BUST THEM NOW! I'VE GOT TO PEE!

SHUT UP AND PEE IN YOUR BOOTS LIKE YOU ALWAYS DO WHEN WE'RE ON STAKEOUT! THIS COULD BE REALLY IMPORTANT!

INSIDE, FAT FREDDY MARVELS AT THE MODERN HEAD SHOP, WITH ITS TRIPLE-BEAM BALANCES, PLATFORM SCALES, AND A PANORAMA OF PARAPHERNALIA OF ALL KINDS.

WOW! LOOK AT ALL THIS STUFF! THINGS SURE HAVE CHANGED!

CAN I HELP YOU, SIR?

SCALES
SCALES
SCALES

AHEM, UH... YES! I WANT A SCALE TO WEIGH GRAMS OF PARAKEET SEED FOR MY UNCLE ARTIE!

HEH HEH, OF COURSE, SIR! WHAT YOU WANT, IT WOULD SEEM, IS OUR TRIPLE BEAM BALANCE, ACCURATE TO A TENTH OF A GRAM UP TO 610 GRAMS, MORE OF COURSE WITH THE EXTRA WEIGHTS, OR PERHAPS, IF IT IS THE SORT OF PARAKEET SEED THAT GOES UP YOUR NOSE, YOU MIGHT BE INTERESTED IN OUR CENT·A·GRAM BALANCE, ACCURATE TO THE HUNDREDTH OF A GRAM...

...THEN AGAIN IF YOU SOMETIMES HAVE NEED OF WEIGHING LARGE AMOUNTS OF (AHEM) "PARAKEET SEED," YOU MIGHT LOOK AT ONE OF OUR PLATFORM BALANCE SCALES, SOME OF WHICH HANDLE UP TO 300 POUNDS!

49

50

OPEN FIRE, MEN!

BOOM! BOOM! DADADADADA BLAM! BLAM!

FIVE MINUTES OF UNINTERRUPTED FIRING LATER:

OKAY, YOU DIRTY SMUGGLERS... D.E.A. HERE! YOU'RE SURROUNDED! COME OUT WITH YOUR HANDS UP!

OH, NO! THERE WASN'T SUPPOSED TO BE ANYONE IN THAT PLANE! WE WERE SUPPOSED TO HAVE MURDERED THEM ALL BEFORE WE ORDERED THEM TO SURRENDER! THOSE POOR INNOCENT GUYS MUST BE SCARED TO DEATH! WE'D BETTER CATCH THEM AND EXPLAIN IT WAS ALL A MISTAKE BEFORE THEY GET TO SOME CHEAP LAWYER AND HARRASS US!

WAIT! STOP! HALT! WE CAN EXPLAIN!

HMM. I'M TOO FUCKED UP TO GO RUNNING THROUGH THOSE WOODS! I'LL JUST GO SIT DOWN INSIDE THAT PLANE AND WAIT UNTIL THOSE CLOWNS COME BACK SO I CAN COLLECT MY **PAY!**

I'LL BE DARNED! IT'S LOADED TO THE GUNWALES WITH **REAL DOPE!**

I MUST BE DREAMING! **TOP QUALITY WEED! COCAINE! OPIUM!**

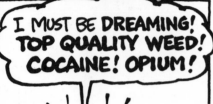

BANG!

NOPE, NOT DREAMING!

SNORT

THOSE FOOLS ARE GOING TO BE BACK AT ANY MOMENT, AND UNFORTUNATELY I CAN'T FLY A PLANE!

...BUT MAYBE I CAN **DRIVE** A PLANE!

WITH THE **WINGS UP**, IT SHOULDN'T BE MUCH WIDER THAN A **L.T.D.!**

WHIRRRR CHUFF CHUFF WHIRR

THERE SEEMS TO BE A **DIRT ROAD** OVER THERE, LEADING **OUT OF THE CLEARING!**

BUMP

BUMP BOUNCE

VROOOMMMMM!

PHINEAS SOON FINDS HIS WAY OUT OF THE WOODS AND BACK ONTO THE EXPRESSWAY TOWARD HOME.

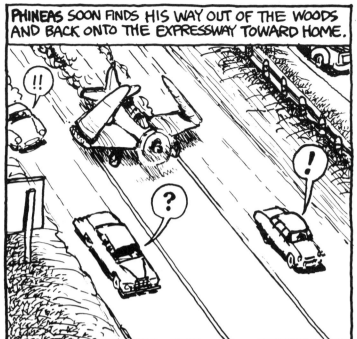

SLAM

CLICK

YOU'LL NEVER **GUESS** WHAT AN INCREDIBLE **FIND** I MADE!

CRASH

HE JUST WENT INTO THE HOUSE NEXT TO THAT DOUBLE-PARKED **ROCKET!**

HOT DAMN! MAYBE EVEL KNIEVEL'S BEHIND THIS! I ALWAYS WANTED TO NAIL THAT SHOW-OFF!

JUST LET ME DUMP THIS **PEE** OUT OF MY BOOT AND LET'S **NAIL 'EM!**

HOP HOP

53

IF ONE OF YOU FOOLS HAS **COME DOWN** ENOUGH TO **FOLLOW INSTRUCTIONS,** I KNOW HOW TO FLY A PLANE! I FLEW THAT **SAME DAMN THING** OFF OF AIRCRAFT CARRIERS BACK IN **WORLD WAR TWO!**

HOLD IT! WE'RE D.E.A.!

SMASH

54

ALL RIGHT! **YOU** DRUNK CLOWNS ARE OBVIOUS VICTIMS OF **OVERWORK, FATIGUE,** AND THE **L.S.D.** THEY PUT IN THAT **GREEN BEER FACTORY** AT THE OTHER END OF TOWN!

YOU THREE ARE **TEMPORARILY SUSPENDED** UNTIL YOU COME TO YOUR **SENSES!**

NOW, THE QUICKEST CURE FOR YOUR PRESENT HALLUCINATORY STATE OF MIND IS TO GO INTO THE LAVATORY AND, ONE BY ONE, PUT YOUR HEAD DOWN THE TOILET WHILE ANOTHER OF YOU FLUSHES IT, IF YOU CAN **MAKE** IT THAT FAR!

WE'LL TAKE OVER FROM HERE!

AGENTS FRANKLIN AND PHINEAS, GATHER UP THE **EVIDENCE!** FREDDY, PUT ME ON YOUR SHOULDER! YOU'RE GOING TO BE **PILOT!**

PUT THE **WINGS** DOWN, AND BEFORE WE **TAKE OFF,** GIVE ME TWO HUGE SNORTS OF THAT **COCAINE!**

UH, EXCUSE ME, UNCLE ARTIE, BUT, UH... HOW DOES ONE **GIVE** COCAINE TO A PARAKEET?

55

IDIOTS! LOOK! SEE THESE TWO TINY HOLES, ONE ON EACH SIDE OF MY BEAK? SEE THOSE? OKAY! YOU STICK A GOD DAMN STRAW PACKED WITH COKE IN THOSE HOLES AND THEN YOU **BLOW!**

FLAPS UP! PUNCH THIS, CLICK THAT, AND HEAD FOR **SPUDVILLE!** WE'RE GOING TO SEE **AUNT SALLY!**

BUT UNCLE ARTIE, SHE TURNED YOU INTO A **PARAKEET!**

DON'T WORRY, NEPHEW! SHE'LL DO **ANYTHING** FOR SOME GOOD **OPIUM!** SHE'LL CHANGE ME BACK! LET'S GO!

WHOOPS! WATCH THOSE **POWER LINES!**

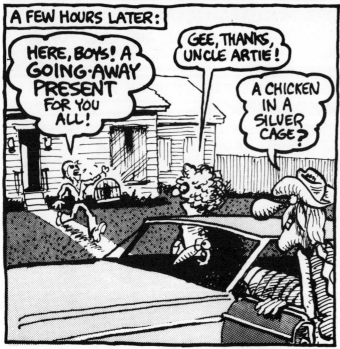

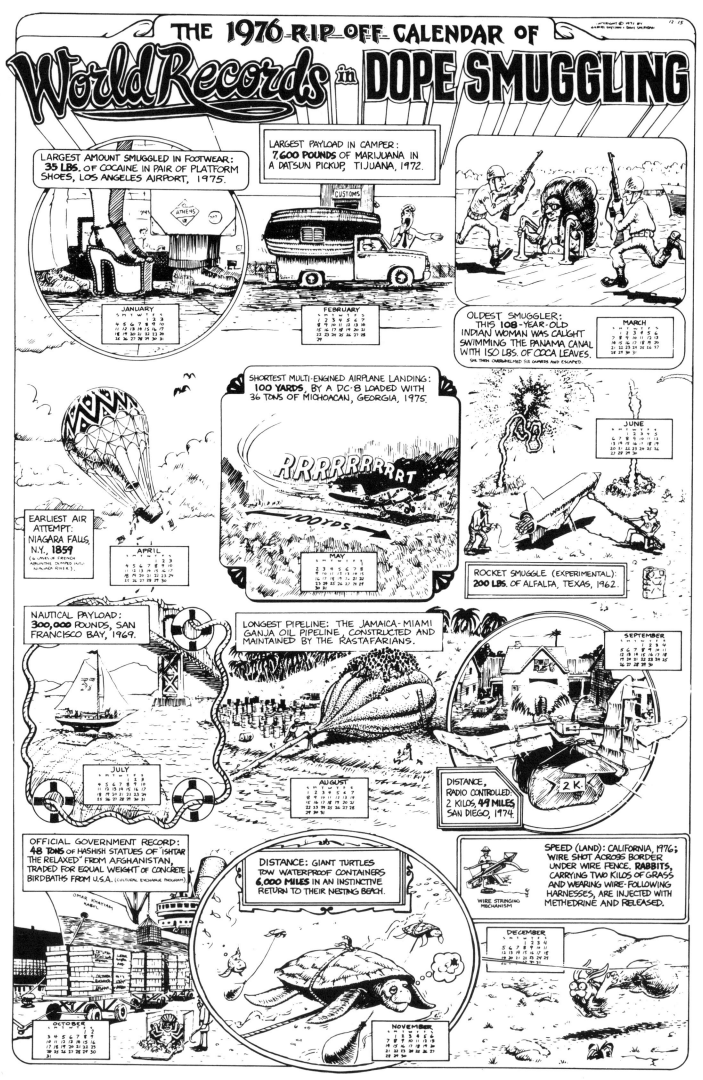

57

NERDS

E-Z-TO-BUILD-NERD FEEDER

60

(GASP!) IT'S A **LITTLE OLD LADY!**

C'MON, SONNY! I WANT TO BUY THESE BOOKS ON HOW TO MAKE **HASH OIL** OUT OF **GRASS!** EVER SINCE I TORE OUT THOSE WORTHLESS GODDAM ROSES AND PUT THE GREENHOUSE TO GOOD USE, I'VE GOT MORE **MARIJUANA** THAN I KNOW WHAT TO DO WITH!

SAY, SONNY, YOU EVER RUN A STORE BEFORE? I DON'T THINK SO! HOW WOULD YOU LIKE TO HAVE A **BUSINESS PARTNER?** I COULD TELL YOU HOW TO MAKE THIS PLACE INTO A **WINNER!**

HELP ME, AND IT'S **HALF YOURS!** WHAT HAVE I GOT TO LOSE?

FIRST OFF, WHY ARE ALL THOSE PEOPLE BLOCKING THE SIDEWALK IN FRONT OF YOUR SHOP?

THEY'RE STANDING IN LINE TO SEE "SPACE-CRAZED," THAT NEW SCIENCE-FICTION MOVIE THAT'S PLAYING DOWN AT THE BIJOU!

WELL, JUST STICK A COUPLE OF THESE LITTLE **HASH PIPES** TOGETHER AND PRESTO! AN "OUTER SPACE PIPE!" STICK ONE OF THESE DIFFRACTION CRYSTALS ONTO THIS SILVER SPOON AND YOU HAVE A "COSMIC COKESPOON!" DO YOU GET THE BASIC IDEA?

NOW GET OUT IN FRONT AND HAWK THIS STUFF! I'M GOING TO TAKE THAT **ISOMERIZER** HOME AND TEST OUT THE SON OF A BITCH!

GET YOUR ALL-WEATHER HASH GEAR! SPECIAL **WINDPROOF** SNORTING SYSTEMS! ALL THE LATEST IN **STONED AGE** TECHNOLOGY!

(WOW! I'M MAKING LOTS OF MONEY NOW! THOSE PEOPLE STANDING IN LINE ARE SO BORED THEY'LL SPEND MONEY ON **ANYTHING!**)

HI'YUH, MAN! FAR OUT PLACE YOU GOT HERE!

UH... CAN I HELP YOU GENTLEMEN?

WE'LL LEVEL WITH YOU, MAN! WE REPRESENT A GROUP OF INVESTORS OPENING UP A NATIONAL CHAIN OF HEAD SHOPS CLOSE TO THEATRES SHOWING "SPACE-CRAZED!" AH, SINCE YOURS IS ALREADY **OPEN,** WE ARE PREPARED TO OFFER **FOUR TIMES** OUR **USUAL SUM!**

FOR GOODWILL!

62

PHINEAS, THERE ARE FIVE LAWYERS, ELEVEN BILL COLLECTORS, AND A LITTLE OLD LADY IN A WHITE ROLLS-ROYCE WAITING TO SEE YOU!

A LITTLE OLD LADY?

PHINEAS! I WENT BY OUR STORE AND THEY TOLD ME YOU HAD SOLD IT! WHAT'S ALL THIS?

"OUR" MOVIE COMPANY!

MOVIE COMPANY? YOU BROKE YET?

FLAT!

WELL, LISTEN! I'VE MADE A DOLLAR OR TWO OFF OF THAT GALLON OF HASH OIL I MADE WITH THE ISOMERIZER, SO I'LL PAY OFF THESE PEOPLE BEFORE THEY STOMP YOU FLAT! BUT I WANT YOU GIVE UP ALL THIS HOLLYWOOD TINSEL, DRUGS, AND SEX, AND COME TAKE A JOB IN MY NEW COMPANY!

A JOB?

I WANT YOU TO BE OFFICIAL TASTER FOR **MOM'S HASH-OIL BROWNIES**! YOU KNOW, THIS STUFF'S GONNA BE **LEGALIZED** SOON AND WE HAVE TO BE READY!

JUST REMEMBER OUR MOTTO, "YOU CAN TRUST MOM!"

I'M LEAVING YOU A BUSHEL OF MY FINEST SINSEMILLA SOAKED IN MY SPECIAL HASH-OIL SAUCE! DROP BY THE HOUSE NEXT WEEK AND WE'LL START COOKIN!

HOME, JAMES!

WOW! YOU'LL NEVER BELIEVE ALL THE THINGS THAT HAPPENED TO ME TODAY! BUT FIRST, LET'S SMOKE A JOINT OF THIS SINSEMILLA SOAKED IN SPECIAL HASH-OIL SAUCE!

WHERE ARE THE CIGARETTE PAPERS?

CIGARETTE PAPERS?

I FORGOT THE CIGARETTE PAPERS!

THE END!

NERDS

FLASH! SAN FRANCISCO HAS JUST BEEN HIT BY A DEVASTATING **EARTHQUAKE**! THE CITY IS IN RUINS! FIRE AND SMOKE EVERYWHERE! 8.5 ON THE RICTOR SCALE!

...PANIC HAS GRIPPED THE CITY AND LOOTERS ARE **RAMPANT**!

LET'S GO!!

WOW!

WOOOEEE!!

OH BOY!

FAR OUT!

COPYRIGHT © 1975 BY SHERIDAN AND SHELTON

BANG!

GNK!

WHAT DID YOU DO THAT FOR?

WE HAVE ORDERS TO **SHOOT** ALL LOOTERS!

WELL, DON'T SHOOT ME! I DON'T EVEN OWN A **LUTE**!

THE END

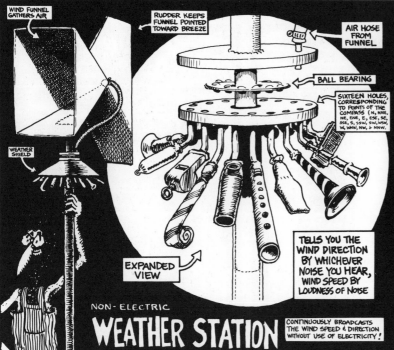
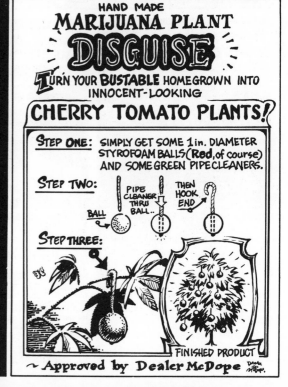
64

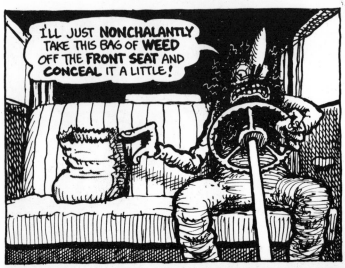

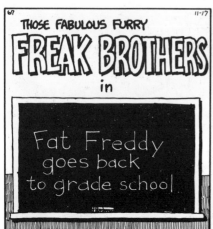

68

A LITTLE OLD LADY IS RIDING THE BUS.

THE DAILY POOP
MORE VIOLENCE ON CITY BUSES

VIOLENCE ON THE BUS!!?

IT'S FAT FREDDY, HALF DRUNK AND EXHAUSTED AFTER BEING FORCED TO STAND IN LINE ALL DAY AT THE UNEMPLOYMENT OFFICE.

COPYRIGHT © 1976 BY GILBERT SHELTON & DAVE SHERIDAN

PLOP

WITHOUT WARNING, THE LIGHTS IN THIS BUS SUDDENLY GO OUT ON A DARKENED STREET.

THE LITTLE OLD LADY PANICS, WHIPS OUT A TEAR GAS PEN, AND SQUIRTS FAT FREDDY IN THE FACE.

HEARING THE BLIND THRASHINGS OF THE HORRIFIED FAT FREDDY, THE DRIVER ALERTLY LOCKS THE DOORS.

ARRRGH!

THUMP! CRASH!

THE REMAINING PASSENGERS EITHER OPEN FIRE WITH THEIR OWN PISTOLS AND TEAR GAS GUNS, OR THROW THEIR MONEY INTO THE AISLE TO SAVE THEMSELVES.

BLAM

POW

IN THE CONFUSION, FAT FREDDY ESCAPES.

AN OPEN WINDOW! (GASP!) I'VE ESCAPED! I'M ALIVE!

ALL TOAD

AT THIS MOMENT, THE LIGHTS GO ON AGAIN.

THE HOLDUP GANG IS GONE, BUT THEY DROPPED ALL OF THE MONEY!!

THAT'S MY MONEY!

NO! THAT'S MINE!

IT BELONGS TO ME!

MINE!

GIMME!

THE NEXT DAY:

DID YOU SEE THIS?

YEAH, I READ ABOUT IT!

I'M NEVER GONNA RIDE THAT CITY BUS AGAIN!

THE DAILY POOP
STILL MORE VIOLENCE
HOLDUP, RIOT ON CITY BUS

72

THE FABULOUS FURRY FREAK BROTHERS in THE 4th FREAK BROTHER!

BY GILBERT SHELTON & PAUL MAVRIDES
COPYRIGHT © 1978 BY GILBERT SHELTON

OUR STORY BEGINS ONE MORNING AFTER A TYPICAL ALL-NIGHT PARTY AT THE FREAK BROTHERS' APARTMENT.

OH, MY ACHING HEAD! I MUST HAVE SNORTED A WHOLE OUNCE OF COCAINE LAST NIGHT!

GASP! WHEEZE! I'M COMPLETELY DEHYDRATED FROM SMOKING ALL THAT GRASS AND HASH! MY VOCAL CORDS ARE TOTALLY DESICCATED!

OOOOOH! OUCH! MY NOSE HURTS FROM WHEN I FELL FLAT ON MY FACE BREATHING LAUGHING GAS!

SOMEONE'S STILL HERE!

HE PASSED OUT IN THE CORNER!

WHO IS IT?

ZNORK

I DUNNO... HE LOOKS SORT OF FAMILIAR, THOUGH...

OH, **THAT** GUY! HE'S BEEN AROUND EVER SINCE I CAN REMEMBER! HE MUST BE OKAY!

PHNZRCK HUMUH.

HUNH? WHANH? WHERE **AM** I?

WHO AM I ??

NEVER MIND! JUST HAVE A HIT OF THIS!

I STILL DON'T REMEMBER WHO I AM, BUT NOW IT DOESN'T SEEM TO MATTER!

THAT'S ALL RIGHT! YOU CAN HANG OUT HERE UNTIL YOU GET YOUR HEAD TOGETHER! THE **FABULOUS FURRY FREAK BROTHERS** ARE ALWAYS READY TO LEND A HAND TO A FELLOW OUTCAST FROM SOCIETY!

73

YOU GUYS ARE THE **FABULOUS FURRY FREAK BROTHERS**? I... I THINK I'VE **HEARD** OF YOU! YOU GUYS ARE **FAMOUS**!

I'VE NEVER EVEN **TALKED** TO A FAMOUS PERSON IN MY WHOLE **LIFE**, AND SUDDENLY HERE I FIND MYSELF **LIVING** WITH **THREE** OF THEM!

I FEEL SO **PROUD**!

WELL, WE COULD USE ANOTHER GOOD MAN AROUND HERE! CAN YOU COOK?

ER, UH... SOMEONE ELSE HAS ALWAYS DONE THE COOKING FOR ME, I GUESS! I DON'T KNOW ANYTHING ABOUT IT!

CAN YOU FIX CARS? THE FRAMMITZ IS ZILCHED OUT ON OUR VAN!

NO, I'VE NEVER WORKED ON A CAR, AS FAR AS I CAN REMEMBER!

CAN YOU TYPE? KEEP BOOKS? USE A CALCULATOR?

I DON'T KNOW! WHAT'S A "CALCULATOR?"

ANYWAY, I THINK WE SHOULD TAKE HIM ALONG ON THE BIG DOPE RUN TODAY! HE MUST BE GOOD FOR SOMETHING!

COME ON, ACE, WE GOT FIVE HUNDRED POUNDS OF BOLIVIAN BOO COMING IN ON THE GREYHOUND THIS AFTERNOON! WE COULD USE SOME TECHNICAL ASSISTANCE!

SURE, FELLOWS! GLAD TO BE OF HELP IN ANY WAY I CAN!

SPROING

MEANWHILE, A SERIES OF EVENTS THAT IS TO HAVE A DRAMATIC EFFECT ON OUR HIRSUTE HEROES IS UNFOLDING DOWN AT CITY POLICE HEADQUARTERS.

I WISH THE PAPERS WOULD STOP MAKING SUCH A BIG DEAL ABOUT THAT OFFICER O'MULLET DISAPPEARING! NOW THEY'RE SAYING IT MIGHT HAVE BEEN A KIDNAPPING!

IF I KNOW MIKE O'MULLET, HE PROBABLY JUST WANDERED OFF SOMEWHERE AND GOT LOST!

COP STILL GONZO! HOW MANY MORE?

CHIEF

I DON'T THINK O'MULLET WOULD LET ANYONE KIDNAP HIM! SOMETIMES I THINK MAYBE HE LEFT PART OF HIS BRAIN OVER THERE IN VIETNAM, BUT HE'S A GOOD COP! HE WOULDN'T HAVE GOT HIMSELF KIDNAPPED!

THE NEWSPAPER IS GIVING THIS DEPARTMENT A REPUTATION AS AN EASY MARK! CON MEN AND SHAKEDOWN ARTISTS FROM ALL OVER THE COUNTRY WILL BE FLOCKING HERE JUST TO SEE WHAT THEY CAN PULL!

SWAK

RING!

HELLO?

LISTEN CLOSELY. THIS IS TERRORISTS, INCORPORATED AND WE ARE HOLDING YOUR OFFICER O'MULLET!

IF YOU DO NOT LEAVE $100,000 CASH IN A LADIES' PURSE BEHIND THE CANDY MACHINE IN THE GREYHOUND STATION BEFORE THREE THIS AFTERNOON, WE ARE GOING TO **EXECUTE** OFFICER O'MULLET WITH A SINGLE 38 CALIBER BULLET TO THE BRAIN!

...AFTER, OF COURSE, WE FORCE HIM TO PERFORM **UNNATURAL SEX ACTS** WITH A **FOUR HUNDRED POUND YORKSHIRE SOW**! HA HA HA!

...AND ALSO AFTER WE GIVE HIM A **JALAPEÑO** AND **LSD ENEMA**! HEE HEE HEE!

...AND ALSO AFTER WE MAKE HIM EAT **POODLE CA-CA**! GIGGLE GIGGLE!

DO YOU THINK THEY BELIEVED US?

NAW! YOU LAID IT ON WAY TOO HEAVY! DON'T YOU GUYS HAVE ANY SENSE OF SUBTLETY OR UNDERSTATEMENT?

NOW WHAT CAN WE DO FOR ENTERTAINMENT? HEY, "FUCKFACE AND THE MICROCEPHALICS" ARE PLAYING OVER AT THE ASSHOLE INN! DO YOU THINK YOU CAN GET YOUR MOM TO DRIVE US OVER? IT'S IN THE PLEASANT VALLEY SHOPPING CENTER!

75

MEANWHILE, AT THE BUS STATION:

THE WOMEN'S PURSE WITH THE MONEY IS IN PLACE BEHIND THE CANDY MACHINE, CHIEF!

THERE WASN'T TIME TO ROUND UP ANY PHONY CURRENCY, SO I HAD TO BORROW SOME **REAL** CASH FROM THE **PETTY GRAFT FUND**! I HAD TO PROMISE THEM WE'D BE **REAL CAREFUL** WITH IT!

AND NEARBY, REFLEXES ARE BEING HONED AND TUNED IN PREPARATION FOR THE SOON-TO-ARRIVE DISGUISED SHIPMENT OF WEED.

WE'LL NEED TO BE ALERT! WE GOTTA SCAN THE PLACE FOR STAKEOUTS!

HOWEVER, WE MUST BE COOL AND STRAIGHT-LOOKING ENOUGH TO AVERT SUSPICION WHEN PICKING UP OUR SHIPMENT OF "COSMETICS!"

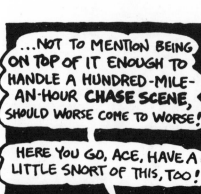

...NOT TO MENTION BEING ON TOP OF IT ENOUGH TO HANDLE A HUNDRED-MILE-AN-HOUR **CHASE SCENE**, SHOULD WORSE COME TO WORSE!

HERE YOU GO, ACE, HAVE A LITTLE SNORT OF THIS, TOO!

WHAT IS THIS STUFF?

IT'S OUR SPECIAL "CRISIS CRANK!" HALF COCAINE, HALF QUAALUDES!

SNORT!

SO, INTO THE STATION COME THE FABULOUS FOUR.

BELCH

 76

THOSE ARE THE **ONES**, CHIEF! MY **UNERRING** SENSE OF CRIMINALITY TELLS ME SO!

CANDY? NAH...

...BUT THEY'RE WALKING RIGHT PAST THE **CANDY MACHINE**! THEY'RE COMPLETELY **IGNORING** THE "DROP!"

THEY'RE EITHER **SCOUTING THE PLACE** OR IT'S A **DIVERSIONARY TACTIC**! THEY CAME HERE FOR THAT **MONEY**! I KNOW!

KEEP DOWN, SERGEANT! WE'LL HAVE TO **WAIT** THEM OUT!

TV

GOT A SHIPMENT FOR "MR. GREEN" HERE TODAY?

JUST A MINUTE! I'LL LOOK!

FAS ASA DOG SHIP

HERE IT IS! NOW, WHICH ONE OF YOU IS "MR. GREEN?"

HE IS!

HE IS!

HE IS!

I AM?

YOU KNOW, I'VE WAITED **YEARS** FOR AN OPPORTUNITY TO PRACTICE THE **HIGHLY SPECIALIZED SKILLS** I LEARNED IN THE **SERVICE**... HOW TO **FRACTURE SKULLS** WITH A **FLICK** OF THE **ELBOW**... HOW TO **SEVER SPINES** WITH A DEFT APPLICATION OF THE **HEEL**... HOW TO **PARALYZE** USING THE **LITTLE FINGER**...

... AND I'M EVEN **BETTER** WHEN I'M **ARMED!** I CAN SHOOT THE **LEGS** OFF **FLIES** AT A **HUNDRED YARDS**, SO THE **SPACE** BETWEEN YOUR AVERAGE **COP'S EYES**, ALTHOUGH QUITE **NARROW**, IS LIKE A **BARN DOOR** TO **ME!**

IN A FEW SHORT SECONDS, O'MULLET THE MAD KILLER COP HAS WIPED OUT THE CREAM OF THE CITY POLICE DEPARTMENT.

THAT'S SHOWIN' 'EM, HUH, BROTHERS? RIGHT **ON**, HUH?

BROTHERS?

79

BUT THE FABULOUS THREE ARE ALREADY A NUMBER OF MILES AWAY, AND THE DISTANCE WILL CONTINUE TO GROW!

WE CAN **SLOW DOWN** NOW! I'M PRETTY SURE HE'S NOT COMING!

SHH! AT LEAST, LET FRANKLIN KEEP CARRYING THE BOX UNTIL HE GETS TIRED!

AND SINCE NO WITNESSES WERE TO BE FOUND, OFFICER O'MULLET WAS NOT ONLY PROCLAIMED A **HERO**, BUT HE GOT TO KEEP THE PURSE FULL OF **MONEY**, WHICH CURED HIM FOREVER OF BEING A **HIPPIE**.

SITE OF HEROIC POLICE SHOOTOUT 1978

IT **WAS** INSTRUMENTAL, HOWEVER, IN HIS LATER BECOMING A **TRANSVESTITE**.

THE END